JUST-RIGHT
leveled readers

Let's Play Football

CO-ALS-220

by Liza Charlesworth
illustrated by Barbara Bongini

ISBN: 978-1-338-33303-9

Text copyright © 2019 by Liza Charlesworth
Illustrations copyright © 2019 Scholastic Inc.

10 9 8 7 6 5 4 3 2 1   19 20 21 22 23

Printed in the U.S.A.   40
First printing 2019

Series design by Maria Mercado

SCHOLASTIC INC.

I am Bob.
Tom and Deb are on
my flag football team.

Min, Sam, and Max are on the other team.

We put on our flags.

We are ready to play.

One, two, three, hike!
Tom hikes the ball to Deb.

Deb passes the ball to me.

I run with the ball.

Oh no!
Min got my flag.

Tom hikes the ball to Deb again.

Deb passes the ball
to me.

I run with the ball.

No one gets my flag.

Oh yes!
I get a touchdown.

Yippee!

Comprehension Boosters

1. Why does Bob say "Oh no!" on page 9?

2. Why does Bob say "Oh yes!" on page 14?

3. Have you ever played flag football or watched a football game? Talk about it.